PRACTISE TOGETHER SERIES

MATHSKILL 1

Games and puzzles for Maths practice

Peter Smith

A Piccolo Original
Piccolo Books

A note to parents

Mathskill 1 is designed for children between the ages of 7–9 years. This age range is, of course, approximate and should not be taken as a rigid guideline as children's maths skills develop at very different rates.

This book has been designed to complement and reinforce much of the maths taught at school, and it uses an informal and lively approach. It contains a variety of activities, puzzles and games especially designed to practise skills such as adding, subtracting, multiplication and measuring.

The instructions should be clear enough to allow the child to do the activities on his own or with a friend, but as your involvement and interest is of the greatest importance, there are notes for parents which explain the aim of the activity and provide suggestions for further practice.

The activities are there to be enjoyed. When they stop being fun, it is time for a rest and a change. Each activity has several examples and can therefore be tried more than once and at more than one session. Encourage the child to find the answers by using the maths he knows, by trial and error and by logical thinking. It is better to think the answer through rather than just guess it.

Before the child starts the activities, collect the following items:
☆ stiff card (empty cereal packets, tissue boxes etc.)
☆ coloured counters (buttons, bottle-tops, tiddly-winks)
☆ coins
☆ crayons, pencils
☆ dice
☆ spare paper
☆ a ruler

There is a pull-out section in the centre of the book to help the child make the necessary items to play *Can you make 12?* (p.16) and *Three in a row* (p.17).

Enjoy the book **together** – the greater the enjoyment, the more your child will relax and gain confidence, and the more he is likely to learn from it.

All answers can be found on pages 31 and 32.

Here are Odd and Even who will guide you through the book.

SNAKE IN THE GRASS

For 1 player

See if you can spot the pattern in each snake's tail and then continue it by using your powers of addition. Odd and Even have done one for you.

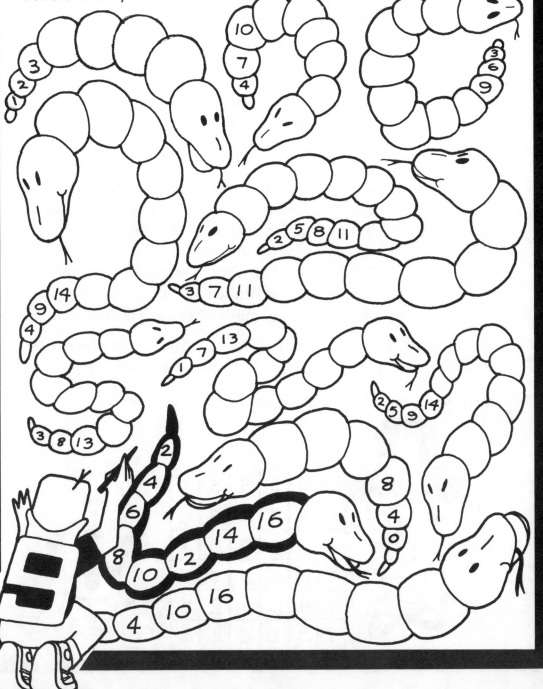

CAN YOU MAKE 12 ?

For 2, 3 or 4 players

You'll need to add quickly to play this game.

You'll need:
* the grid (see opposite)
* 42 tiles (you can make these by turning to the centre pull-out section)
* 30 counters each for 2 players – a different colour for each player (less if 3 or 4 of you are playing).

How to play:
* Cover all the numbers on the grid with the tiles.
* Toss a coin to decide who starts.
* Starter: remove two tiles and add the two numbers together.
* If they add up to 12, keep the tiles and put a counter on both the numbers you uncovered.
* If they don't, then replace the tiles.
* Partner: now it's your turn.

* Hint:
* Try to remember what numbers have been uncovered and where they are on the grid. This will help you to make 12 when it is your turn.

Now, using the rules for making 12, try to make 10 and draw up your own grid (see below). Here, you will need 36 tiles to play.

☆ The winner is the one with the most counters on the grid.

Making 10

0	3	5	9	6	1
5	7	2	10	8	4
6	1	8	9	5	3
2	10	3	5	0	7
4	9	10	6	2	5
7	5	0	8	1	4

1	4	8	0	9	2
6	12	5	7	3	10
10	6	2	12	6	11
7	1	9	8	12	4
11	3	6	5	0	6
2	6	11	10	7	1
4	8	0	9	5	3

Parent note: Here the child will need to use his knowledge of number bonds with speed and accuracy, but let him add using counters or a number line for as long as he needs to. Encourage the child to work out what number is needed to make 12 (or 10) before uncovering the second number. How about asking the child to uncover three numbers to make 12 (or 10)?

THREE IN A ROW

For 2 players

This game is like noughts and crosses.

You'll need:
* a grid (see below)
* 2 sets of 9 answer cards (you can cut these out of the centre pull-out section of the book).

2+1	4+3	1+1
2+2	3+2	4+4
5+4	3+3	1+0

grid

answer cards

How to play:
* Toss a coin to decide who starts.
* Starter: choose a square and cover it with the correct answer card from your set.
* The other player may challenge and if correct, the player challenged misses his turn.
* Partner: now you choose a square and cover it with your correct answer card.
* Carry on playing like noughts and crosses.

The winner is the first to get three correct answer cards in a row (either down, across or diagonally).

6+6	2+7	3+8
1+6	6+9	7+7
9+4	8+2	5+3

Answer cards

9 + 3	9 + 9	4 + 6
9 + 8	8 + 5	6 + 9
7 + 4	7 + 7	8 + 8

17, 11, 12, 18, 16, 14, 10, 15, 13 → **Answer cards**

Answer cards → 30, 18, 9, 27, 6, 21, 15, 24, 12

9 × 3	6 × 3	4 × 3
5 × 3	3 × 3	8 × 3
10 × 3	2 × 3	7 × 3

Parent note: In this activity the child is using his knowledge of number bonds and 2, 3 and 5× tables in order to win the game. You could make the game more difficult by using the 6, 7, 8, 9× tables.

BOXED IN

For 2 players

See how many boxes you can make.

You'll need:
* the grids below
* a pencil.

How to play:
* Toss a coin to decide who starts.
* Starter: join one dot to another (either across or down but not diagonally).
* Partner: now it's your turn.
* Each player has to try to make a box from the lines drawn on the grid by joining up the fourth side of the box, like this
* If one of you makes a box, write your initial inside it and have another 'go'.
* When all four games have been played, add up the scores.

The winner is the one with the most boxes.

1

Player 1 =   boxes

Player 2 =   boxes

2

Player 1 =   boxes

Player 2 =   boxes

3

Player 1 =   boxes

Player 2 =   boxes

4

Player 1 =   boxes

Player 2 =   boxes

Score sheet

PLAYER 1		PLAYER 2	
GAME	BOXES	GAME	BOXES
1		1	
2		2	
3		3	
4		4	
TOTAL		TOTAL	

Parent note: This game provides practice both in adding up and how to score. Encourage the child to think about where he is drawing his lines so he can try to make as many boxes as possible.

9

For 1 player

Test your detective powers by decoding these sentences and then see if you can guess what country they describe.

If you give each letter in the alphabet a number you can make up a simple code:

a	b	c	d	e	f	g	h	i	j	k	l	m	n	o	p	q	r	s	t	u	v	w	x	y	z
1	2	3	4	5	6	7	8	9	10	11	12	13	14	15	16	17	18	19	20	21	22	23	24	25	26

Just add up the two numbers, write in the answer and then the letter it stands for. Easy!

1

9 +9	3 +2	2 +2	11 +12	5 +3	5 +4	9 +11	3 +2	0 +1	9 +5	3 +1	1 +1	6 +6	19 +2	4 +1
18														
R														

2

17 +3	3 +5	4 +1	17 +2	4 +1	8 +11	12 +8	3 +6	1 +2	6 +5	7 +12	0 +1	14 +4	3 +2	16 +4	1 +0	13 +6	6 +14	14 +11

18	4	3	1	6	8	11	0	9	4	3	9	16	10	6	4	6	8	3
+2	+4	+2	+0	+6	+8	+8	+1	+9	+1	+3	+6	+2	+9	+5	+5	+3	+6	+4

1	3	2	3	7	4	2	16	11	2	14	12	8	9	14	19	4	0	7
+2	+5	+3	+2	+12	+1	+7	+3	+11	+3	+4	+13	+8	+6	+2	+2	+8	+1	+11

3	6	5	3	8	0	9	4	5	0	15	4	7	7	3	8	1
+3	+12	+10	+4	+11	+1	+9	+1	+0	+1	+5	+1	+7	+1	+2	+10	+4

Now, write down the name of the country you think these sentences describe.

Parent note: Children are fascinated by codes and should therefore do the addition with enthusiasm. If the child adds up incorrectly then the sentence will not make sense, so there is an element of self-correction here. The child could make up different sentences to try out on a friend.

FIGURE IT OUT

For 1 player

These puzzles are just like crossword puzzles except that the clues are given in numbers instead of words. Use a pencil to begin with just in case you make a mistake. Use a calculator if you like or work difficult clues on scrap paper.

1

Across	Down
1. 7 + 7	1. 8 + 9
3. 4 + 5	2. 2 + 2
4. 2 + 5	3. 6 + 3
5. 1 + 1	5. 10 + 10
6. 15 + 15	6. 16 + 15
7. 13 + 8	7. 2 + 0
8. 5 + 3	8. 4 + 4

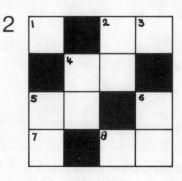

2

Across	Down
1. 4 + 3	1. 10 − 3
2. 69 + 24	2. 55 + 44
4. 100 − 31	3. 1 + 2
5. 46 − 16	4. 19 + 41
6. 2 + 3	5. 46 − 8
7. 5 + 3	6. 96 − 39
8. 111 − 64	8. 20 − 16

Puzzle 3

Across
1. $17 + 14$
3. Subtract 53 from 1000
6. $500 + 125$
8. $44 + 48$
9. $515 + 514$
11. $1 + 1$
12. $100 - 47$
13. $10 - 7$
14. $9 + 9$
16. $35 + 55$
17. $33 + 18$
18. $195 + 195$

Down
1. $17 + 19$
2. $60 + 61$
3. $20 - 11$
4. 1000 minus 501
5. $26 + 46$
7. $207 + 298$
10. $40 - 17$
11. $135 + 80$
13. $125 + 175$
15. $34 + 47$
16. $100 - 1$
18. $100 - 97$

3

Puzzle 4

Across
1. $112 + 41$
4. $32 + 24$
6. $12 + 18$
7. $124 + 124$
8. $5 + 3$
9. $270 + 160$
10. $194 + 343$
11. $2 + 2$
12. $350 + 271$
13. $8 + 16$
14. $23 + 36$
15. $153 + 153$

Down
1. $65 + 73$
2. $25 + 25$
3. three
4. $175 + 365$
5. $43 + 25$
7. $62 + 175$
9. $140 + 291$
10. $232 + 297$
11. $183 + 263$
12. $27 + 38$
13. $17 + 3$
15. $1 + 1 + 1$

FIGURE IT OUT

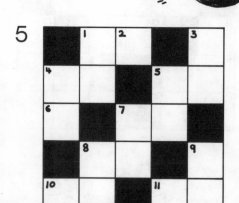

5

	Across	Down
1.	7 + 8	8 + 7
3.	1 + 2	3 + 2
4.	13 + 12	18 + 14
5.	11 + 11	17 + 6
6.	2 + 1	14 + 13
7.	19 + 18	16 + 15
8.	23 + 18	22 + 22
9.	1 + 0	9 + 9
10.	21 + 13	2 + 1
11.	14 + 14	1 + 1

Across / Down column detail:

Across
1. 7 + 8
3. 1 + 2
4. 13 + 12
5. 11 + 11
6. 2 + 1
7. 19 + 18
8. 23 + 18
9. 1 + 0
10. 21 + 13
11. 14 + 14

Down
1. 8 + 7
2. 3 + 2
3. 18 + 14
4. 17 + 6
5. 14 + 13
7. 16 + 15
8. 22 + 22
9. 9 + 9
10. 2 + 1
11. 1 + 1

Across
1. 240 + 146
4. 100 minus 25
6. 45 + 16
7. Subtract 544 from 1066
8. 4 + 3
9. 222 + 526
10. 10 − 5
11. 999 − 916
12. 61 + 2
13. 21 − 2
15. 23 + 3
16. 200 − 30
17. 7469 + 1594
20. 3 + 6

Down
1. 4065 minus 390
2. 73 + 8
3. 3 + 3
4. Subtract 237 from 965
5. 25 + 27
7. 600 − 57
9. 350 + 433
12. 523 + 137
13. 10 + 7
14. 1000 − 91
15. 100 − 71
16. 11 + 2
18. 10 − 4
19. 100 minus 97

6

On the next page you will find the tiles for
Can you make 12? and *Three in a row.*

STICK
THIS PAGE
ON TO SOME
STIFF CARD

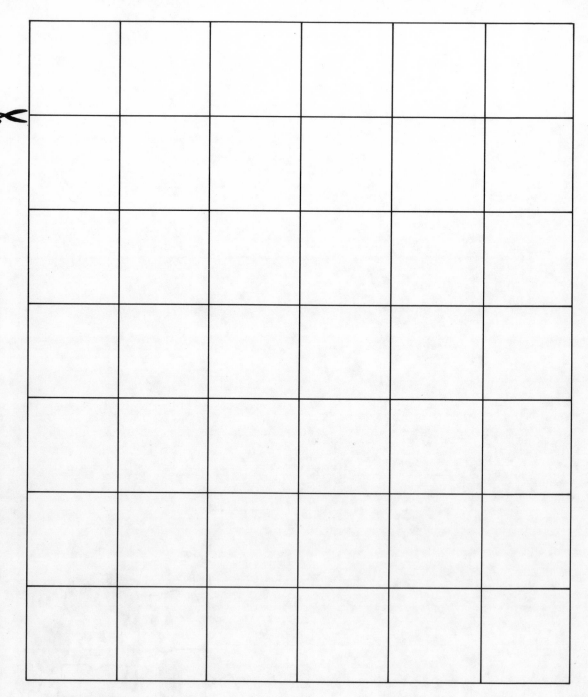

Instructions

You will need the blank tiles to play *Can you make 12?* and the
numbered tiles to play *Three in a row*.

For *Can you make 12?* just stick down this page on to some stiff
card and cut along the lines.

For *Three in a row*, stick down the opposite page with the
numbered side up and cut along the lines. One player
should choose the white set of tiles, the other player, the grey set.

14	11	7	14	11	7
9	10	8	9	10	8
12	15	13	12	15	13
17	11	12	17	11	12
18	16	14	18	16	14
10	15	13	10	15	13
30	18	9	30	18	9
27	6	21	27	6	21
15	24	12	15	24	12

STICK
THIS PAGE
ON TO SOME
STIFF CARD

THROW A WORD

For 2 players

This is a bit like Scrabble, but in this game you throw a die to collect the letters to make a word.

You'll need:
* a grid (see next page)
* a die
* a piece of paper and a pencil.

How to play:
* Toss a coin to decide who starts.
* Starter: throw the die twice; the first throw gives the number for moving across (easting), the second for moving up (northing).
  Example: in the first game, a 3 followed by a 2 gives you the letter 'e'.
* Partner: now your turn.
* Write your letters on a piece of paper.
* Do this 6 times each.
* Now make words using as many of the 6 letters as you can. You can use each letter as many times as you like.
* You score points for each correctly spelt word.

Score sheet

6 letter word = 7 points
5 letter word = 5 points
4 letter word = 4 points
3 letter word = 3 points
2 letter word = 2 points

The winner is the player with the highest number of points.

Parent note: This is an enjoyable way to encourage children to learn how to build words. There is an element of chance which should provide encouragement for less gifted players. Note that there are more vowels in game 1 and that the other 4 games have an increasing number of consonants to make the word building more difficult.

6	h	i	w	o	e	z
5	m	a	u	g	v	f
4	e	b	o	t	u	j
3	c	i	n	a	r	q
2	o	s	e	k	y	d
1	l	a	u	p	i	x
START HERE	1	2	3	4	5	6

Northing ↑

Easting ⟶

6	u	l	b	a	j	p
5	e	s	k	z	h	n
4	m	w	o	g	c	i
3	i	d	p	r	l	x
2	f	a	v	o	y	m
1	n	k	u	t	e	a
START HERE	1	2	3	4	5	6

Top grid

	1	2	3	4	5	6
6	b	a	r	f	o	n
5	g	c	e	w	z	s
4	u	l	d	i	p	q
3	m	o	h	a	y	c
2	d	e	t	x	s	j
1	i	k	b	u	v	t
START HERE	1	2	3	4	5	6

Easting →

Northing ↑

Bottom grid

	1	2	3	4	5	6
6	b	f	c	w	d	u
5	e	g	i	j	o	k
4	l	r	m	a	n	h
3	h	p	i	r	f	a
2	s	e	t	o	g	v
1	a	x	w	y	u	z
START HERE	1	2	3	4	5	6

For 1 player

On the grids below you have to fill in the missing signs. You will need a plus (+) or minus (−) sign to reach the answer. Remember you have to fill in the missing sign downwards as well as across. Use a pencil to begin with just in case you make a mistake.

Grid 1:

3		4	→	7
	■		■	
5		6	→	11
↓	■	↓	■	↓
8		10	→	18

Grid 2:

6		38	→	44
	■		■	
35		19	→	54
↓	■	↓	■	↓
41		57	→	98

Grid 3:

98		53	→	45
	■		■	
39		14	→	25
↓	■	↓	■	↓
59		39	→	20

Grid 4:

50		14	→	36
	■		■	
13		9	→	4
↓	■	↓	■	↓
37		5	→	32

Puzzle 1 (top left):

63		28	→	35
	■		■	
19	■	17	→	2
↓	■	↓	■	↓
44		11	→	33

Puzzle 2 (top right):

86		39	→	47
	■		■	
48	■	19	→	29
↓	■	↓	■	↓
38		20	→	18

Puzzle 3 (bottom left):

7		16	→	23
	■		■	
28	■	9	→	19
↓	■	↓	■	↓
35		7	→	42

Puzzle 4 (bottom right):

3		17	→	20
	■		■	
16	■	5	→	11
↓	■	↓	■	↓
19		12	→	31

Parent note: Look at the way the child tackles these puzzles and help him to think about what he is doing. Try to prevent him from just guessing the answer (see 'A note to parents' on p.2).

CODEQUIZ

For 1 player

Use your 2, 3 or 5× tables to decode these clues. Then see if you know the answers . . .

If you give each letter in the alphabet a number you can make up a simple code:

a	b	c	d	e	f	g	h	i	j	k	l	m	n	o	p	q	r	s	t	u	v	w	x	y	z
18	2	4	35	24	50	25	60	12	40	27	6	9	16	20	33	14	22	15	10	30	45	8	55	36	5

Here the letters of the alphabet are represented by a multiple of 2, 3 or 5.

Just multiply the two numbers, write in the answer and then the letter it stands for.

1

2×5	5×12	3×8	2×2	3×6	3×11	4×3	2×5	2×9	2×3	5×4	10×5	3×6	5×6	3×5	2×5	11×2	2×9	3×2	2×6	3×6
10																				
T																				

Answer _ _ _ _ _ _ _ _

2

2×9	3×10	5×2	12×5	4×5	11×2	2×10	10×5	4×5	2×3	3×4	5×9	6×4	2×11	5×2	2×4	6×2	5×3	5×2

Answer _ _ _ _ _ _ _   _ _ _ _ _ _ _

24

6×3	2×1	2×11	3×4	7×5	8×3	2×8	12×2	2×12	5×7	3×5	2×10	8×2	3×8

Answer — — — — —

3×5	3×3	9×2	3×2	2×3	4×2	3×4	2×8	5×5	8×3	7×5	6×2	8×2	5×3	12×2	2×2	5×2

Answer — — —

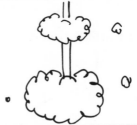

6×3	3×3	4×5	10×3	8×2	2×5	9×2	6×2	4×4	2×5	12×5	2×9	5×2	3×8	11×2	6×5	11×3	5×2	3×5

Answer — — — — — — — —

Parent note: This activity will provide good practice in the three multiplication tables that the child should know thoroughly.

KALEIDOSCOPE

For 1 player

If you really know your tables, you can make these fascinating patterns inside a circle.

Here is how Odd and Even did one.

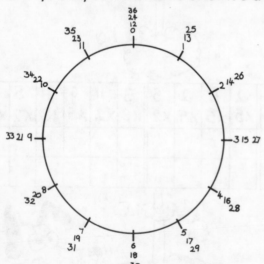

4 × table

* Odd chose the 4× table.
* Even divided the circumference of a circle into twelve equal segments.
* Odd numbered each segment 0–11 (clockwise).
* Using her ruler, Even joined the multiples of 4 (starting at 0).
* What did Odd and Even find inside the circle?

Now you try to finish this one! It's a bit more complicated . . .

* Here you have to use the 5× table.
* Continue numbering the segments until you reach 65 (Odd and Even stopped at 36).
* Now using a ruler join the multiples of 5.
* What pattern have you made this time?
* Why don't you colour it in to make a bright pattern?

Parent note: This activity should be read over and discussed between you and the child before he starts. Make sure he understands the meaning of circumference, segment, multiple and sequence. You can trace over the lines of the pattern so that the sequence of the multiples is understood and reinforced.

Now do these two using your 2 and 3× tables. Here the circles have been divided into 10 segments, and are already numbered for you. What do you notice each time?

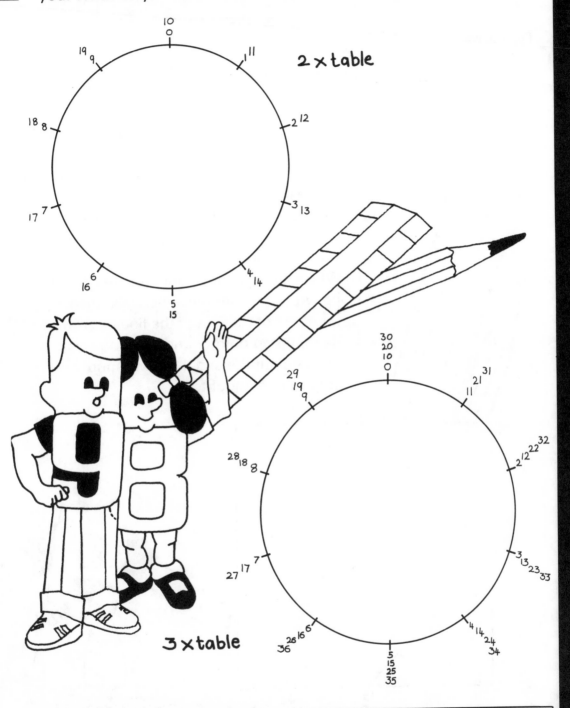

2 × table

3 × table

Parent note: When the child has done these, he could make some patterns using circles divided into 8 segments using the 2, 3 and 5× tables.

SQUARE DANCE

For 1 player

Use your powers of subtraction to make these patterns in a square.
You'll need: * a ruler

Here is what Odd did: * In a large square, Odd chose 4 numbers
between 0 and 20: 15, 4, 17 and 2.

(1) * He wrote one of the numbers at each corner
of the square.

(2) * He found the mid-point of each line by using
a ruler and joined the 4 points to make a
second square.

(3) * Where the second square touches the first,
he wrote the difference between the 2
numbers at the end of the line (e.g. 15−4=11).

* He repeated point 2, and went on doing
this until, at the end, he saw a final
pattern of 4 noughts.

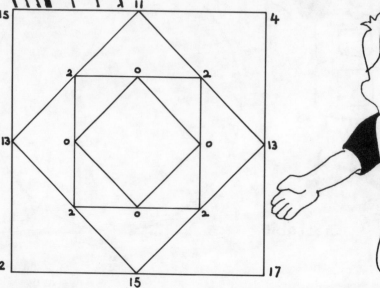

Conclusion:
The pattern for subtraction in a square resulting from the numbers
15, 4, 17 and 2 is four noughts and it took four squares to reach it.

Now you try these. They get more difficult as you go along . . .
Remember to write your conclusion after finishing each pattern.
The first one has been started for you.

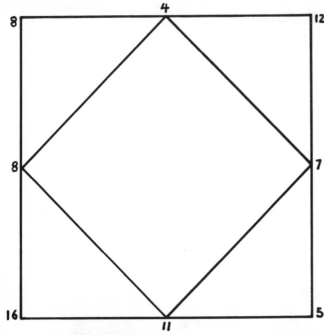

Conclusion:
The pattern for subtraction
in a square resulting from
the numbers 8, 12, 5 and 16
is . . .

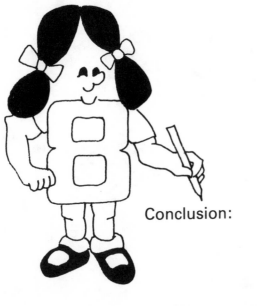

Conclusion:

2 _____ 7

8 _____ 17

Parent note: This activity encourages the child to look for pattern and in the process he practises subtraction bonds. It requires some patience and guidance but the child should enjoy drawing his own squares and the measuring work is valuable experience. The child can continue this activity by drawing his own squares on a piece of paper and choosing four numbers between 0 and 20.

DOTTY DOTS

For 1 player

Work out the sums first, then join the dots by starting at the lowest answer. What have you drawn?

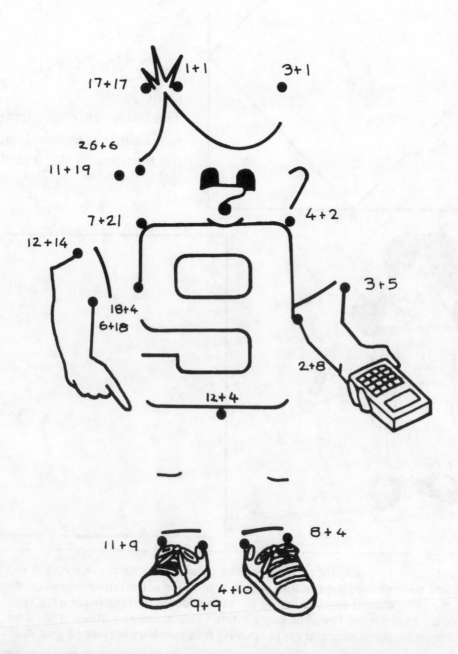

ANSWERS

Snake in the grass p. 3

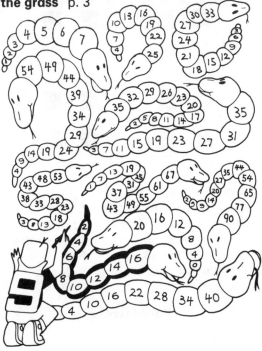

Solve it p. 10
1. Red, white and blue   (French flag)
2. These sticks are tasty   (French sticks = bread)
3. The Alps are for skiing   (French Alps)
4. Cheese is very popular   (Brie, Camembert etc)
5. Frogs are eaten here · (Frogs' legs)
   Country = FRANCE

Figure it out p. 12

1

2

3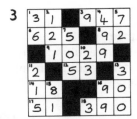

4

5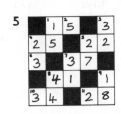

6

Sign here p. 22

3	+	4	→	7
+		+		+
5	+	6	→	11
↓		↓		↓
8	+	10	→	18

6	+	38	→	44
+		+		+
35	+	19	→	54
↓		↓		↓
41	+	57	→	98

63	−	28	→	35
−		−		−
19	−	17	→	2
↓		↓		↓
44	−	11	→	33

86	−	39	→	47
−		−		−
48	−	19	→	29
↓		↓		↓
38	−	20	→	18

98	−	53	→	45
−		−		−
39	−	14	→	25
↓		↓		↓
59	−	39	→	20

50	−	14	→	36
−		−		−
13	−	9	→	4
↓		↓		↓
37	−	5	→	32

7	+	16	→	23
+		−		+
28	−	9	→	19
↓		↓		↓
35	+	7	→	42

3	+	17	→	20
+		−		+
16	−	5	→	11
↓		↓		↓
19	+	12	→	31

Codequiz p. 24

1 The capital of Australia = Canberra
2 Author of Oliver Twist = Charles Dickens
3 A bride needs one = Groom; dress
4 Small winged insect = Fly
5 A mountain that erupts = Volcano

Kaleidoscope p. 26

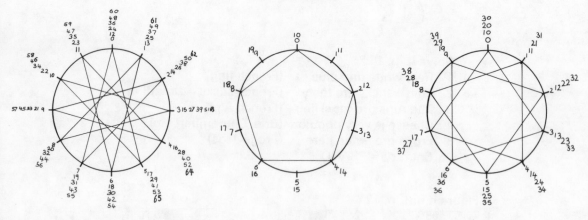

Square dance p. 28

1 The pattern resulting from 8, 12, 16 and 5 is four noughts in five squares.
2 The pattern resulting from 8, 2, 7 and 17 is two noughts and two 'twos' in five squares.

Dotty dots p. 30
You have drawn Odd